Snoopy has wit and wisdom
To cover everything —
Whether you're in the doghouse,
Or you have the world on a string!

With Many Friendly Thoughts from

_____

The Wit and Wisdom of Snoopy

by Charles M. Schulz

Hallmark

Contents

On Coming Home

On Sympathizing

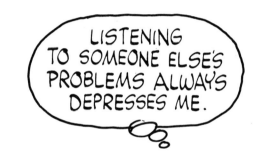

On Anticipation

Other Peanuts Philosophers by Charles M. Schulz

THE MEDITATIONS OF LINUS
LUCY LOOKS AT LIFE
CHARLIE BROWN'S REFLECTIONS

LINUS ON LIFE
SNOOPY'S PHILOSOPHY
THE WORLD ACCORDING TO LUCY
THE WISDOM OF CHARLIE BROWN

Editorial Direction: Arnold Shapiro
Design: William Hunt and David Jenkins